This book b...

Gruffalo Explorer

....

Autumn

For Jesse Hall and in memory of his big brother, Skye Hall.

Autumn is a great time of year to head outside and see the world change around you. Trees go from green to red, yellow and brown and lose their leaves, while animals get ready for the cold winter ahead by making the most of all the nuts and berries. You could stock up on some berries, too – autumn is the best time to go blackberry picking!

Head outside and see what you can find, but don't forget to take this guide with you to record your discoveries!

Don't forget your wellies!

If you don't have a shell, take an umbrella!

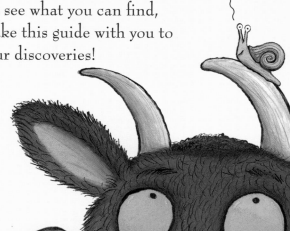

Signs of Autumn

Conkers

Red leaf

Yellow leaf

Squirrel

Tree stump

Feather

Bare branches

Mushroom

Acorns in cups

EXPERT EXPLORERS

Blackberries

Hedgehog

Sycamore seeds

Take a stroll through the deep dark wood . . .
Look at all the pictures below. How many can you see?
Put a Gruffalo paw sticker next to each one.

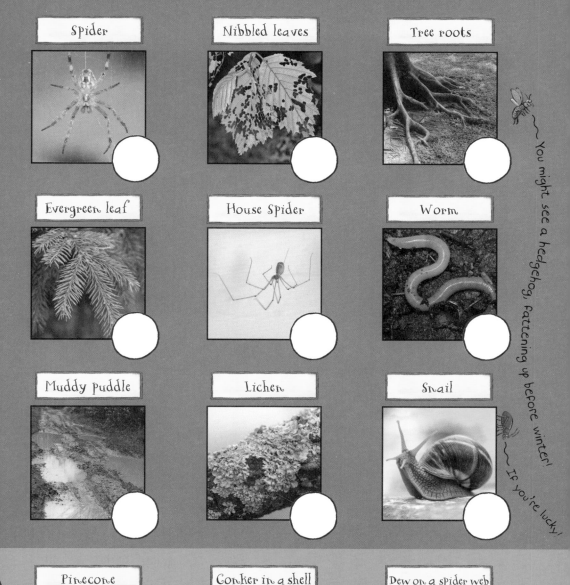

Spider

Nibbled leaves

Tree roots

Evergreen leaf

House Spider

Worm

Muddy puddle

Lichen

Snail

You might see a hedgehog, fattening up before winter!

If you're lucky!

Pinecone

Conker in a shell

Dew on a spider web

Autumn Colour

Autumn is a time when leaves change colour and fall from the trees. For every leaf you find, choose the matching colour sticker and stick it in the right box!

Bright red

Orange

Brown

Dark red

Yellow

It's hard work for a tree to keep its leaves looking good. In the autumn many trees drop their leaves so they can save energy to survive the long winter

Sticker Tree

Using your sticker page, cover this tree in autumn leaves!

Did you know?

Leaves are green because of a pigment called chlorophyll, which catches sunlight and turns it into the energy a tree needs to grow. But it takes so much energy to make chlorophyll that in winter the tree stops producing it, the green colour fades and new colours show through.

Leaf Detective

Once leaves have dropped to the floor they are easy to collect, so find as many as you can and see if you can tell what kind of tree they fell from. Use the leaf guide below to help you, then put a leaf sticker next to each one you find.

Elder

Holly

Silver Birch

Oak

Horse Chestnut

Beech

Maple

Hawthorn

Hazel

Leaf Art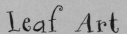

Collecting leaves is great fun and there are
so many things you can make with them,
whether it's decorations, bunting,
cards or amazing pieces of art!

Leaves can be a little damp
when you pick them up, so
first press them flat and
leave them to dry.

You can place them
between the pages of a
newspaper with a weight
on top and soon they'll be
perfectly pretty and flat.

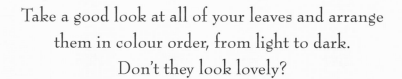

Take a good look at all of your leaves and arrange
them in colour order, from light to dark.
Don't they look lovely?

Leaf Art

Just look at what else you can make
using your dried leaves and a little paint!

A fabulous fish...

Some bright bugs...

How about some leaf bunting?

You can even make some woodland hats. Simply paint some animal faces onto a long strip of card, adding eyes, nose and whiskers where needed, then glue the card into a circle and add leaves to create ears or antlers!

Fluffy feathers make perfect rabbit ears

Autumnal Art

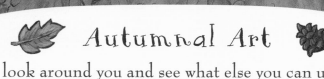

Take a look around you and see what else you can use to create some fun nature pictures. You can leave your picture on the floor for other Nature Explorers to discover.

You can use leaves, flowers, feathers, moss, twigs, stones and grass. Gather up as many different objects as you can, choose different colours and textures and see what you can create.

Transform a Leaf

Using your pencils or stickers, see what you can turn these leaves into.
A butterfly, a snail, a cheerful bird – or maybe even a dragon?

Brilliant!

That's not a leaf, it's a conker

Berry Pretty

In autumn you'll see many fruits and berries growing. They all contain the seeds of a plant, from which new plants grow. They are also an important source of food for animals and birds over the winter months. How many berries can you see? Place a special sticker by each one.

Blackberries
These grow on brambles.

Rosehips
These grow on dog rose shrubs.

Elderberries
These grow on elder trees.

As the weather gets colder and food becomes harder to find, many birds fly south to warmer countries like Africa

This is called migration!

Holly Berries

These grow on holly bushes and trees.

Rowan Berries

These grow on rowan trees.

Sloe Berries

These grow on blackthorn trees.

Hawthorn Berries

These grow on hawthorn hedges.

Ivy Berries

These grow on ivy vines.

Mud Painting

You'll find mud everywhere, both dry and squelchy wet,
especially if it's been raining! So find some paper,
add some water and get creative!

You can use sticks or
brushes to paint with.
But you will get messy!

I ♥ Conkers

Conkers

Everyone loves conkers so keep your eyes peeled and see how many you can collect. If you've found some then you've also found a horse chestnut tree.

Horse chestnut trees produce flowers.

2

1

The flowers are pollinated by insects.

3

Oh, I get it

After pollination the flower develops into a shiny brown conker inside a spiky green case.

4

Later these conkers will grow into tiny little trees.

Did you know?

Conkers are poisonous for humans to eat, but squirrels and deer can eat them without feeling sick!

Nuts, Seeds and Cones

In autumn many trees produce nuts, seeds and cones.
This is a clever way for the tree to spread its seeds and from seeds new trees can grow! Put a Gruffalo paw sticker by each seed, nut or cone you spot.

Acorns

These grow on oak trees.

Conkers

These grow on horse chestnut trees.

Sycamore seeds

These grow on sycamore trees.

Why don't you find a nut and bury it?

Then come back another day and see if you can find it!

If you find a sycamore seed, drop it and watch it spin!

Pinecones

These grow on pine trees.

Alder cones

These grow on alder trees.

Larch cones

These grow on larch trees.

Nuts! Have you seen any of these?

Beechnuts

These grow on beech trees.

Hazelnuts

These grow on hazel trees.

Walnuts

These grow on walnut trees.

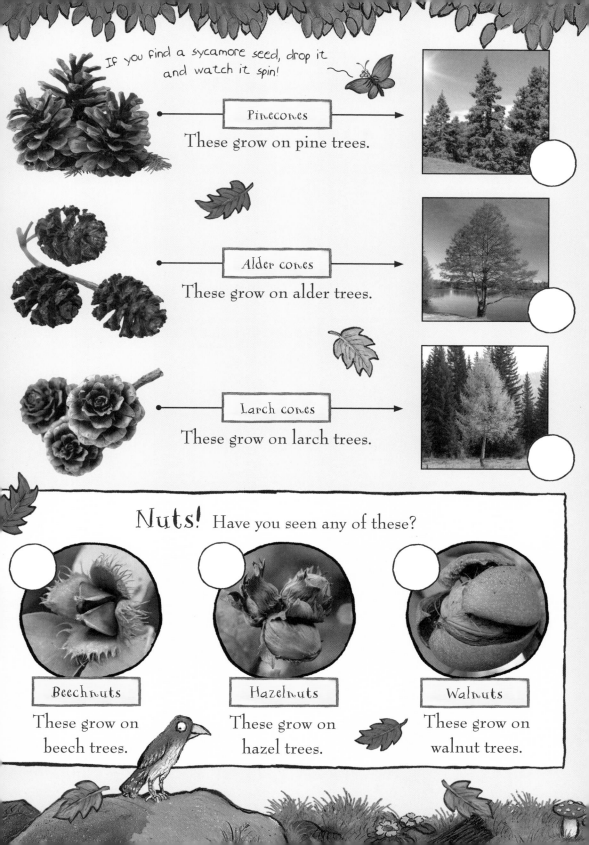

Cone Bird Feeder

You will need: pinecones, ribbon or string, peanut butter, a butter knife, birdseed and scissors.

When the weather gets colder it can be harder for birds to find food, so why not help by making some bird feeders? They're easy to do, they look good and they're tasty (if you're a bird).

Simply take your pinecone and tie ribbon or string to the top of the cone. With an adult to help you, carefully spread peanut butter over the cone, then sprinkle the sticky butter with birdseed and hang in the garden.

If your cone is closed, leave it in a warm place until it opens!

Did you Know?

Cones grow on trees and have lots of seeds inside. When the cones open up, the seeds are released on the wind and scattered all around. From these new trees can grow.

Fungi and Mushrooms

Step into the deep dark wood and see if you can see some mushrooms and fungi. They grow all around us, up and out of the soil or on logs and trees. Put a special mushroom sticker next to each one you see.

The mushroom you see is the flowering part of the fungi growing under your feet.

Bracket Fungus	Common Puff all	Fly Agaric
Parasol Mushroom	King Alfred's Cake	Jelly Ear
	Shaggy Ink Cap	Sulphur Tuft

Spider Spot

When it's cold outside spiders like to
come inside to keep warm.
Have you seen a spider inside your house?
If so, give yourself a special sticker.

I've seen a spider!

Spiders have eight legs, but this poor spider is missing his.
Can you draw them?

Lift a Log, Find a Bug!

All sorts of creatures, like worms, ants, spiders and beetles, can be found under logs. See if you can find a log that's not too heavy and, with an adult to help you, lift it up and look very carefully underneath. What can you see?

Woodlouse

Millipede

Snail

Slug

Worm

Make sure you put the log carefully back in place, exactly as you found it, so the creatures underneath can get comfortable again.

Beetle

If you spot any of the insects shown above, add a bug sticker!

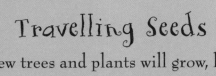

Travelling Seeds

From seeds new trees and plants will grow, but the seeds need to travel far and wide enough to make sure they grow a good distance away from their parents. This is called 'dispersal' and it happens in a number of different ways.

By wind
Winged seeds, like sycamore seeds, can float away on the wind.

By animal
Hungry animals and birds eat fruits and the seeds inside come out in their poo! In this way the seeds get taken to a new place where they can grow.

They arrive inside ready-made fertiliser too!

By hitch-hiking

Some seeds are covered in small hooks or hairs and so they stick to the fur of passing animals and are carried to new places.

By exploding

Some fruits explode as they ripen or if an animal brushes past them. Some seeds even have exploding pods, which means they can all scatter their own seeds!

Make a Seed Bomb!

You too can help disperse seeds and here's how:

This is another messy one. But it's fun!

You need some small seeds like grass seeds or wildflower seeds, which you mix with mud.

Add just enough water to make a fairly solid ball of mud and allow it to dry a little.

Then choose a tree and throw the seed bomb at its trunk. When it explodes the seeds will spread!

Ask an adult to help you!

By being taken away

Animals like squirrels and mice collect hazelnuts and acorns to make winter food stores, often burying them very far from the parent tree.

Explorer Chart

Fill in the explorer chart below – and don't forget
to use your weather stickers to decorate!

I went for a walk today with

. . . .

We went to

. . . .

It was

. . . .

I brought back some

. . . .

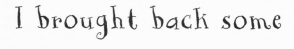

The weather was

. . . .

Design a Pumpkin

Lots of people decorate pumpkins in the autumn.
Draw some below, and decorate them with your special stickers.

~ You'll find eye, teeth and mouth stickers on the sticker page!

~ Ooh, scary!

Nature Notes

Use these pages to stick in things you find, keep photos of your day or
write poems or stories about the things you have seen.

Nature Notes

Nature Notes

 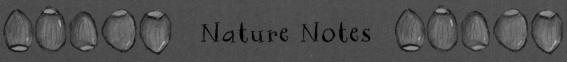

Winter

Winter can be a hard time for wildlife, as the days are short and there isn't much food around. But it can still be a great time to go looking for wildlife because the trees are bare and you can spot things perching on the branches much more easily. Winter is also a good time to look for migrating birds – you might well see ducks, geese and swans braving the cold.

Wrap up warm and see what you can find, but don't forget to take this guide with you to record your discoveries!

Snow doesn't count as a hat!

I'd wear a hat if I were you

Winter Wonders

Icy puddle
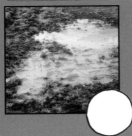

Holly and berries

Tree stump

Wriggly tree roots

Robin

Dead leaves

Drey

Conifer

Old nest
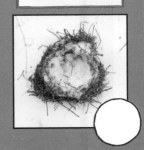

Squirrel nests are called dreys!

Snowflakes

Squirrel
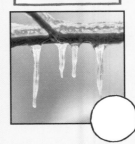

Icicles

Look at all the wintry pictures below.
How many can you see on your stroll?
Put a Gruffalo paw sticker next to each one.

Mistletoe

Feeding birds

Snowy footprints

Nut

Moss

Green lichen

Snowy branch

Pine cone

Bare branches

Your footprints can be the first!

EXPERT EXPLORERS

A frosty leaf

A frosty web

Fresh snow

Fresh snow should be untouched by any foot

Snow Gruffalo

Decorate this snowy scene
and use your stickers to
build a snow gruffalo.

Aha! Oho! A trail in the snow!

The Gruffalo's Child sees three snowy tracks when she's out on her walk. Use your stickers to match the right animal to the right track.

Owl

Snake

Fox

Paw Prints

It's sometimes easier to see animal or human tracks in snow.
Look very carefully – how many of these can you see?
Put a Gruffalo paw sticker next to each one you spot.

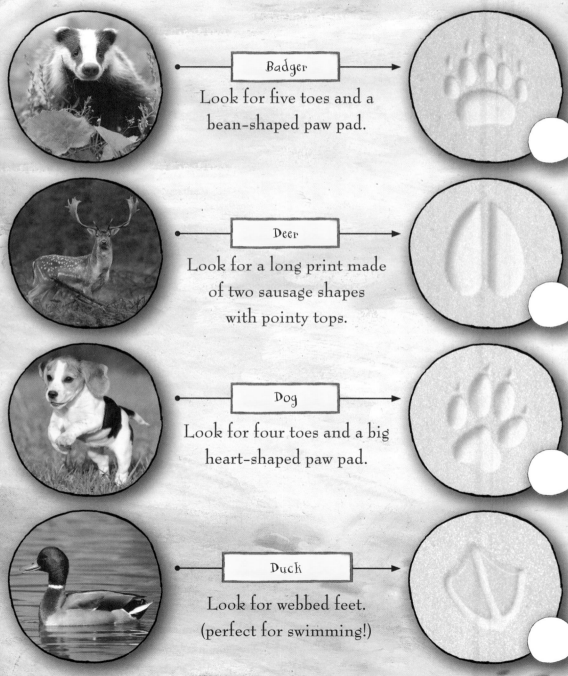

Badger

Look for five toes and a bean-shaped paw pad.

Deer

Look for a long print made of two sausage shapes with pointy tops.

Dog

Look for four toes and a big heart-shaped paw pad.

Duck

Look for webbed feet. (perfect for swimming!)

You can search for footprints in the mud as well as snow!

Fox

Look for four toes and a matching size paw pad.

Bird

Look for thin stick-like marks.

Cat

Look for four toes and a paw pad.

Squirrel

Look for small pads with long claw marks.

The bigger and heavier the animal, the deeper the print it leaves behind.

Animal Tracks

Fill this page with animal tracks! Tracks you've seen or maybe tracks you wish you'd seen. You can use pencils, crayons or maybe even thumbprints.

Tree Faces

Have you ever spotted a face in a tree?
The woods are full of them!

Keep your eyes peeled and see
how many you can spot on
your winter walk.

Who Made That Hole?

Have you ever seen a hole near a tree or in a bank and wondered who lives inside it? Winter is a good time to spot animal burrows or dens, where some animals eat, sleep and raise their offspring. The cold weather often means greenery has died away so you can see the hole clearly. Put a sticker next to each hole that you see.

Water vole

Burrow

Look for small holes in banks of land close to the water's edge. The grass will be shorter around the entrance to the hole.

Fox

Den

These are everywhere in the countryside! Look for food remains outside a single fox-sized entrance.

Mole

Hill

Look for small heaps of mud. Moles don't live in the mud mound, it's a sign that they have tunneled below!

Rabbit

Warren

Look for a rabbit-sized hole on slopes and banks with rabbit droppings near the entrance.

Cosy Cave

The Gruffalo and the Gruffalo's Child live inside a cave.
Use your stickers to decorate the inside of their home.

Where do they come from and where do they go?

The Gruffalo's Child follows the snowy tracks to find
an animal, but where do the creatures below live?
Use your stickers to match the right animal to the right home!

~ Who else do you think lives underground?

Winter Weather Watch

The snow fell fast and the wind blew wild . . .

What is the weather like today? Winter weather changes all the time.
Keep watch and add a sticker for each type of weather you experience!

Snow

Clouds

Clear blue sky

Wind

Fog

Storm

Grey sky

Rain

Hailstones

I'm so cold . . .

Make a Snow Scene

Why not make a pretty snow scene and create your own weather.

You will need:

A clean empty jar, scissors, desiccated coconut and glitter.
To make a nature snow globe you'll need a sponge, pine cones, dried
leaves or twigs. To make a Gruffalo snow globe you'll need white,
black and red modelling clay, tiny twigs and an adult to help you.

Nature snow globe:

Cut the sponge into a dome shape and glue inside
the lid of your jar. If you would like your nature
scene to sparkle just add small dots of glue to your
twigs and leaves and sprinkle with
glitter. Use your scissors to cut little
slots into the sponge and when they are dry,
press your leaves and twigs into the slots.
Remember that your display needs to fit
inside the jar, so don't make it too big!

Add two tablespoons of
desiccated coconut and a
teaspoon of glitter to your jar,
then tightly screw the lid and
the nature display into position.

Turn upside-down and enjoy your snow scene!

Always glue your displays in the centre of
your jar lids. If they are too near the
edge they may not fit inside the jar.

Gruffalo snow globe:

To make a snow gruffalo display, instead of a sponge you'll need white modelling clay.

Roll three balls of clay, with a fourth that's a bit bigger.
Glue the biggest ball inside the jar lid, keeping it away from the edge of the lid, and leave to dry.

Push a twig through the three small balls, leaving about 2cm at the bottom which you push into the larger ball.

If you only have white modelling clay you can always use paint to add the snow gruffalo's features!

Glue into position. When the glue is dry you can then begin to shape your snow gruffalo, by adding eyes, teeth, ears, claws and horns. Your tiny twigs make perfect claws!

Make a Gruffalo Snowflake

In winter everything can look quite bare, so why not decorate your window with Gruffalo snowflakes!

You will need:

A4 white paper, small scissors, a pencil, a black felt pen, a ruler, a paper clip, an empty cereal box and an adult to help you.

Start with a 21 cm x 21 cm square piece of paper. Fold corner to corner, like this.

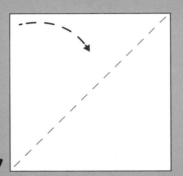

You now have a triangle and you need to fold corner to corner. Do this twice.

Folded edge

Trace this outline onto a piece of paper and glue the traced drawing to card (the back of a cereal packet will do!). Carefully cut away the blacked out areas. This is your template.

Place your triangle of paper here.

Make sure the folded edge is on the left! Now put your template on top and trace around it with your pencil. Cut away the black areas as shown.

Use a paper clip to hold the paper together whilst you trace around it and cut

Fold the face in half and
draw a semi-circle as shown.
Cut the semi-circle out - this
will make the Gruffalo's eyes!

Semi-circle

Folded edge

You could draw his eyes
instead of cutting them

Now carefully unfold the snowflake,
tape it to a window and enjoy!

Hello Spider!

In winter when you're keeping warm inside your house, keep your eyes peeled for these eight legged house guests. Put a sticker next to each one you spot.

Cupboard spider

False widow spider

Cardinal spider

Giant house spider

Zebra jumping spider

Tube spider

Cellar spider

Missing sector orb weaver spider

This spider spins a web where one section is completely missing

If you have seen a spider in your house,
then reward yourself with this badge!
How big was it? Draw it here:

I've seen a spider!

Winter Birds

Some birds migrate in the winter.

Robin

Starling

Chaffinch

Greenfinch

Carrion crow

Magpie

Blackbird

House sparrow

Jay

Barn owl

Black swan

Greater spotted woodpecker

Migration means they fly off to warmer countries once it starts to get cold. But plenty of birds stay all year round. Which ones can you spot? Put a bird sticker next to each one.

Swan

Great tit

Collared dove

Wren

Jackdaw

Rook

Feral Pigeon

Wood Pigeon

Blue Tit

Marsh tit

Coal tit

Green woodpecker

Winter is a great time to spot hungry birds looking for food. The bare branches make them easier to spot!

EXPERT EXPLORERS

Make a Forest

You will need:

green paper, scissors, tape, glue, glitter, a pencil and an adult to help you.

Find something round, like a saucer or a cup, and place it onto your green paper. Use a pencil to trace around the object to create a circle shape, then cut out the circle and cut it in half as shown in the picture.

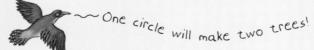 ~ One circle will make two trees!

With the straight edge at the top, take each corner of your semi circle and curl them together until you've made a cone. Tape it together to make a basic tree shape.

Now for the leaves!

You can cut long strips of green paper as shown in the picture and make lots of thin cuts along the strip, being careful not to cut all the way to the top! Then cut three small triangle shapes along the top edge to help the paper curve around the tree.

Glue or tape along the top edge of the strip and stick into position on your tree, starting at the bottom and adding new strips of paper as you work your way up to the top!

Curve your leaves by wrapping them around a pencil!

You can also make leaves by cutting out small triangles of green paper. Use your pencil to curve the bottom of each leaf before gluing or taping them to the bottom of the tree.

Start at the bottom and work your way up – the bigger the tree the more leaves you will need!

You can decorate some of your trees with glitter!

You can also add leaves by drawing them on. Use a colour pencil that's lighter or darker than the green of the tree to make sure they stand out.

~ If you cut out lots of different size circles you will end up with a forest full of different size trees!

Goodbye Winter!

Winter can feel long, but the weather will gradually feel warmer and many signs of spring will soon start to appear. Put a butterfly sticker next to each sign of spring you see.

Frogspawn

Snowdrops

Buds

Blossom

Daffodils

Primroses

Ducklings

Crocuses

Well done, you are now a winter
Gruffalo Explorer!

Reward yourself with a
special sticker like this

I'm a
Gruffalo
Explorer!

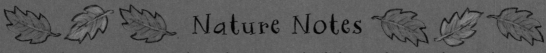

Nature Notes

Use these pages to stick in things you find, keep photos of your day or write poems or stories about the things you have seen.

Nature Notes

Nature Notes

Nature Notes

Nature Notes

Nature Notes